The Doors. Complete Music.

Alabama Song.
Page 226

Back Door Man.
Page 230

Been Down So Long.
Page 9

Blue Sunday.
Page 210

Break On Through.
Page 48

Cars Hiss By My Window.
Page 164

The Changeling.
Page 100

Crawling King Snake.
Page 234

The Crystal Ship.
Page 122

Do It.
Page 44

Easy Ride.
Page 205

The End.
Page 76

End Of The Night.
Page 162

Five To One.
Page 188

Hello, I Love You.
Page 6

Horse Latitudes.
Page 222

Hyacinth House.
Page 96

I Can't See Your Face In My Mind.
Page 181

I Looked At You.
Page 41

Indian Summer.
Page 238

L'America.
Page 70

L.A. Woman.
Page 133

Land Ho!
Page 158

Light My Fire.
Page 3

Love Her Madly.
Page 218

Love Me Two Times.
Page 116

Love Street.
Page 50

Maggie M'Gill.
Page 192

Moonlight Drive.
Page 130

My Eyes Have Seen You.
Page 38

My Wild Love.
Page 212

Not To Touch The Earth.
Page 176

Peace Frog.
Page 54

People Are Strange.
Page 120

Queen Of The Highway.
Page 199

Riders On The Storm.
Page 34

Roadhouse Blues.
Page 154

Runnin' Blue.
Page 80

Shaman's Blues.
Page 59

Ship Of Fools.
Page 127

The Soft Parade.
Page 24

Soul Kitchen.
Page 150

Spanish Caravan.
Page 90

The Spy.
Page 223

Strange Days.
Page 112

Summer's Almost Gone.
Page 196

Take It As It Comes.
Page 144

Tell All The People.
Page 19

Touch Me.
Page 173

Twentieth Century Fox.
Page 87

Unhappy Girl.
Page 202

The Unknown Soldier.
Page 124

The W.A.S.P. (Texas Radio And The Big Beat).
Page 184

Waiting For The Sun.
Page 66

We Could Be So Good Together.
Page 108

When The Music's Over.
Page 213

Wild Child.
Page 16

Wintertime Love.
Page 147

Wishful Sinful.
Page 84

Yes, The River Knows.
Page 168

You Make Me Real.
Page 14

You're Lost, Little Girl.
Page 105

GW00771749

Wise Publications
London/New York/Sydney/Copenhagen/Madrid

Exclusive Distributors:

Music Sales Limited
8/9 Frith Street, London W1V 5TZ, England.
Music Sales Pty Limited
120 Rothschild Avenue, Rosebery, NSW 2018, Australia.

Order No.AM932008
ISBN 0-7119-5184-5
This book © Copyright 1995 by Wise Publications

Book design by Pearce Marchbank, Studio Twenty

Printed in the United Kingdom by
Redwood Books Limited, Trowbridge, Wiltshire.

Your Guarantee of Quality
As publishers, we strive to produce every book to
the highest commercial standards.
The book has been carefully designed to minimise awkward page turns
and to make playing from it a real pleasure.
Particular care has been given to specifying acid-free, neutral-sized paper
made from pulps which have not been elemental chlorine bleached.
This pulp is from farmed sustainable forests and was produced with
special regard for the environment. Throughout, the printing and binding have
been planned to ensure a sturdy, attractive publication which
should give years of enjoyment.
If your copy fails to meet our high standards, please inform us and
we will gladly replace it.

Music Sales' complete catalogue describes thousands of titles and is
available in full colour sections by subject, direct from Music Sales Limited.
Please state your areas of interest and send a cheque/postal order for £1.50 for postage to:
Music Sales Limited, Newmarket Road, Bury St. Edmunds, Suffolk IP33 3YB.

Light My Fire.

The Doors.

Hello, I Love You.

The Doors.

- Repeat and fade -

Been Down So Long.

Words: Jim Morrison. Music: The Doors.

down on your knee; _____

Ba — by, Ba — by,

Ba — by, _____ won't you get down on your

knee. _____

C' — mon, lit — tle dar — lin',

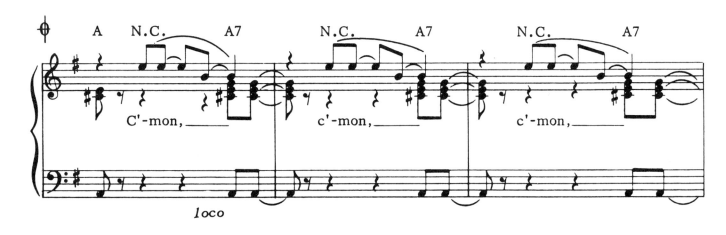

You Make Me Real.

Jim Morrison.

Wild Child.

The Doors.

side.

Drums   Star-ing   in-to   the hol-low id-ol's eye_

Wild   child_

full   of grace_   sav-ior_   of the   hu – man race_

8va basso

your cool face____   your cool   face____

your cool face __

8va   (spoken)

"You remember when we were in Africa"

18

Tell All The People.

Robbie Krieger.

bu – ry all our trou-bles in the sand.   Oh

yeah! _____

Fol – low me a – cross the sea where milk-y ba – bies seem to be

mold – ed flow – ing re – vel – ry   with the one that set them free

Tell All The Peo – ple that you see _____   it's

just me_____ fol-low me down_____

Tell All The Peo-ple that you see_____ fol - low

me _____ fol-low me down.___

Tell All The Peo-ple that_ you see _____ we'll be
fol - low

free _____
me _____

fol-low me down. _____

Fol-low me down, _____ you got to fol-low me down, _____

fol-low me down _____

Tell All The Peo-ple that you see _____ we'll be

free _____ fol-low me down _____

(repeat and fade)

The Soft Parade.

Jim Morrison.

"When I was back there in seminary school,
there was a person there who put forth the
proposition that you can petition the Lord
with prayer ...
petition the Lord with prayer...petition
the Lord with prayer...petition the Lord
with prayer.
You cannot petition the Lord with prayer!"

soft a-sy-lum? I can't make it an-y-more; The man is at the door.

Fast (in 2)

Peppermint miniskirts, chocolate candy,___
Champion sax and a girl named___ Sandy;___

Guitar Solo

There's

on - ly___ four   ways to get un - rav - eled;___
one is___ to   sleep and___ the   oth - er___ is

trav - el,___

Twice as slowly (in 4)

8va _ _ _ _ _ _ _ _ _ _ _ _ _ _ _

1st ce

_____ but it's get-tin' much hard-er.

8va _

2nd ce

Got-ta meet me   at the edge of   town,__

3rd ce

(Half-spoken:)   Trop-ic cor-ri-dor,

8va _

1st ce

You'd bet-ter come a-long.__   Just you and I__

8va _

2nd ce

out-skirts of the cit-y.   We were so a - lone.__

3rd ce

trop-ic treas-ure.

8va _ Fade out

1st ce

Bet-ter bring your gun.__   You'd bet-ter bring your gun._(spoken passage)*

8va _ _ _ _ _ _ _ _ _ _ _ _ _ _ _ _ _ _ _

2nd ce

Bet-ter bring your gun __

3rd ce

(Half-spoken:)   Trop-ic cor-ri-dor,   trop-ic   treas-ure.

*(Spoken ad lib over instrumental)

When all else fails, we can whip the
horses' eyes and make them sleep and
cry.

33

Riders On The Storm.

The Doors.

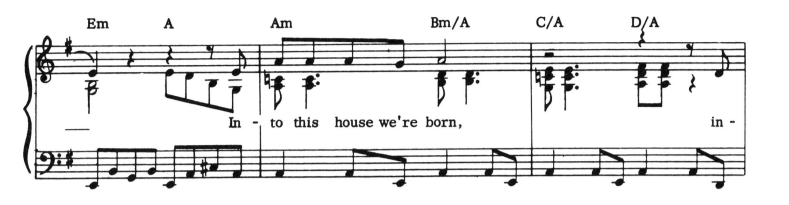

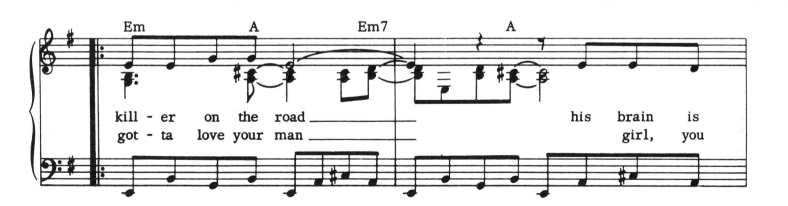

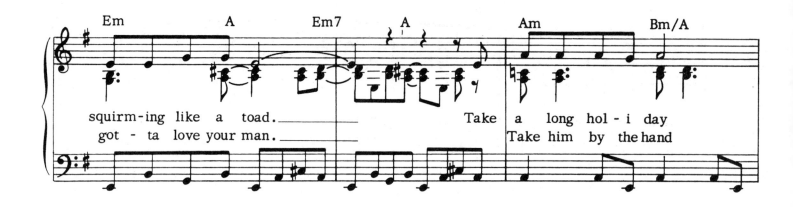

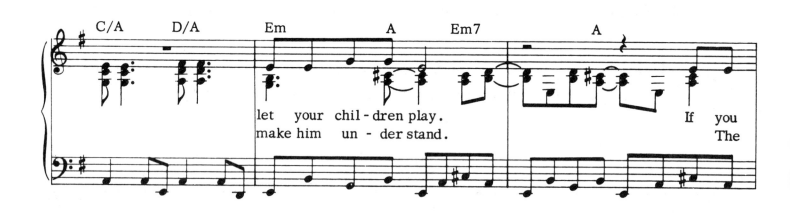

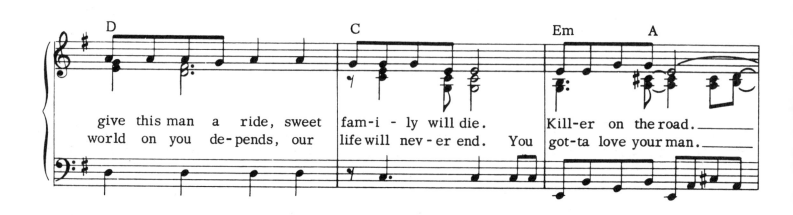

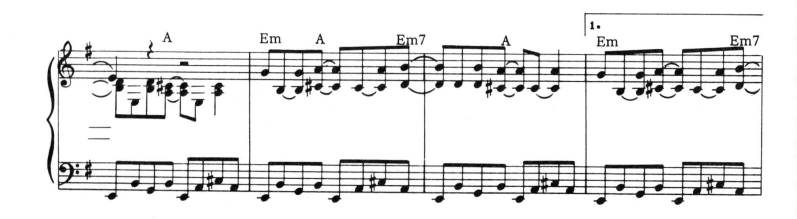

My Eyes Have Seen You.

The Doors.

(repeat ad lib)

I Looked At You.

The Doors.

1. I looked at you _____ You looked at me, ___
2. I walk with you _____ You walk with me, ___

I smiled at you ___
I talked to you ___

You smiled at me ___ }
You talked to me ___ } And we're on our way. ___

No, we can't turn back,___ babe;   Yeah, we're on our way;___

And we can't turn back___   'cause it's too

late,   too late,   too late,   too late,   too

late._____ And we're on our way.___   No, we can't turn back,

Do It.

Jim Morrison & Robbie Krieger.

Please, please, lis-ten to me, chil-dren.

Please, please, lis-ten to me, chil-dren.

You are the ones who will rule the world.

(Drums Solo)

You got-ta please__ me

all ___ night.

sfz

sfz

Break On Through.

The Doors.

With a quick beat

3. I found an island in your arms, a country in your eyes,
   Arms that chain, eyes that lie.... Break on Through, etc.

4. Made the scene from week to week, day to day, hour to hour,
   The gate is straight, deep and wide....Break on Through, etc.

Love Street.

The Doors.

She has robes and she has mon-keys, La - zy dia - mond-stud-ded flunk-ies,

She ___ has wis - dom ___ and knows what to do, ___

She has me and

she has you. ___

She ___ has wis - dom and

knows what to do, ___ She has me and

she   has   you.

repeat 3 times

Spoken:

1. I see you live on Love Street;___   There's the store where the crea-tures meet.
2. I won-der what they do in there,___   Sum - mer Sun - day and a year.___
3. I guess I like it fine so far.___

She lives   on   Love Street, Lin - gers long   on   Love   Street.__

She has__ a house___   and   gar-den   I would like to   see what hap-pens.

(repeat and fade)

53

Peace Frog.

Words: Jim Morrison. Music: The Doors.

Just a - bout the break of day.___

She came, then she drove_ a-way,_

sun-light in her hair._ Blood on the streets runs a riv-er of sad - ness._

Blood in the streets, it's up to my thigh.__

The riv-er runs down the legs of the cit - y;

(Spoken:) Indians scattered on dawn's highway bleeding ghosts crowd the young child's fragile egg-shell mind.

Blood in the streets of the town of New Ha - ven;

Blood stains the roofs and the palm trees of Ven-ice.

Blood in my love _ in the ter-ri-ble sum-mer;_ Blood-y red sun _ of fan -

tas - tic L. A.

Blood screams her brain as they chop off her fin - gers.

Blood will be born__ in the birth of a na -tion;

Blood is the rose of mys-te - ri - ous un - ion.

D.S. al 𝄋

There's

Fmaj7

Shaman's Blues.

Jim Morrison.

Will you give an-oth-er chance? Will you try a lit-tle try?

Please stop and you'll re-mem-ber we were to - geth - er,

an - y way.

All right

Now, if you have a cert-ain even-ing you could lend to me,

Guitar Solo

Voice

Will you stop to think and won - der just what you'll see

out on the train - yard nurs-ing pen-i-ten-tia-ry. It's

gone.   I   cry   out

loco

long. _____

8va -

Did you stop_ to con- si -der   how it will feel,

8va -

cold grind-in' griz-zly bear jaws hot on your heels.

8va -

Do you of-ten stop and whis - per in Sat-ur-day's shore (that) the

loco

63

whole world's a sav-iour, who could ev-er ev-er ev-er ev-er ev-er ev-er

8va

ask for more?

8va

Do you re - mem - ber? Will you stop,

loco

N.C.

Gm   N.C.   Gm   *p*

will you stop   the

N.C.

pain?___   There will

Drums

p   *f*

(Spoken ad lib over instrumental)
He's sweatin', look at him...optical pro-
mise...you'll be dead and in hell before
I'm borne...sure thing...bridesmaid...the
only solution--isn't it amazing?

Waiting For The Sun.

Words: Jim Morrison. Music: The Doors.

Wait - ing, wait - ing, wait - ing, wait - ing. Wait - ing for you to come a - long; Wait - ing for you to hear my song; Wait-ing for you to come a - long;

68

Wait-ing for you to tell me what went wrong.

This is the stran - gest

life I've ev - er known.

Wait - ing for the

sun.

69

L'America.

Words: Jim Morrison. Music: The Doors.

Repeat ad lib

I took a trip down to l'A - mer - i - ca

to trade some beads for a pint of gold.

71

of gold.

l'A-mer-i-ca, l'A-mer-i-ca, l'A-mer-i-ca,_____ l'A-mer-

C'-mon, peo-ple, don't you

without 8va

look so down;_ You know the rain-man's com-in' to town._

He'll change your weath-er, he'll change your luck,_

(without 8va basso)

Friend-ly stran - gers came to town,___

all the peo-ple___ put them down.___ But the wo - men___

loved their ways___ come a-gain some oth - er___

day.___ Like the gen - tle rain,___

like the gen - tle rain___ that falls.___

(with 8va basso)   Repeat ad lib

Getting gradually faster

l'A - mer - i - ca, l'A - mer - i - ca, l'A - mer - i - ca,___

1.
2.

___   l'A -   l'A -

mer   -   i - ca.

sfz

75

The End.

The Doors.

This is the end, beau-ti ful - friend.

This is the end, my on - ly friend, the end of 2. It

our e - lab-'rate plans, the end of ev - 'ry - thing that
hurts to set you free but you'll nev - er fol - low me. (to Coda)

stands, the end, No safe-ty or sur - prise, the end. I'll

nev-er look in-to your eyes a - gain._____

Can you pic-ture__what will be, So__ lim-it-less and

free, des-p'rate-ly in need__ of some stran - ger's

hand, in a des-p'rate land.

Lost in a Ro-man ___ wil-der-ness of

pain, and all the chil - dren

(piano continues to end)

are in - sane; all the chil-dren ___ are in - sane;

wait-ing for the sum-mer rain. _____ There's dan-ger ___ on the

edge of ___ town,   Ride the king's high-way.

Weird scenes in - side the gold mine; ___   ride the king's high-way

west,___ ba - by.   Ride the snake,   to the

lake,   { The an - cient lake.   Sev - en miles;   He's
        { The snake is long,   Ride the snake,

old   and his skin is cold.   The West is the

best.   The West is the best.

Get here   and we'll do the rest.   The blue bus ___

(spoken*)

D.C.

Coda   is call-ing us.___   Dri-ver, where you tak-ing us?___

The end of laugh-ter and soft lies,   The end of

nights we tried to die.   This is the end.___

*The killer awoke before dawn,
He put his boots on,
He took a face from the ancient gallery,
And he walked on down the hall.

He went to the room where his sister lived,
And then he paid a visit to his brother,
And then he walked on down the hall.

And he came to a door,
And he looked inside,
"Father?"
"Yes, son?"
"I want to kill you.
"Mother, I want to...."

Come on, baby, take a chance with us, (3x)
And meet me at the back of the blue bus.

79

Runnin' Blue.

Robbie Krieger.

82

don't fight, too much to lose; Can't fight the Run-nin' Blues.

Wishful Sinful.

Robbie Krieger.

Twentieth Century Fox.

The Doors.

Spanish Caravan.

The Doors.

Ad lib. (Flamenco Style)

Much Slower (in 3)

Em | Am | B | Em
Car - ry me, car - a - van, take me a - way, Take me to

Am | B | Em | Am | Em
Por - tu - gal, take me to Spain, An - da - lu - si - a, with

fields full of grain, I have to see you a - gain and a-

gain. Take me, Span - ish Car - a - van, Yes, I

know you can.

95

Hyacinth House.

Words: Jim Morrison. Music: The Doors.

Hy - a - cinth House ___ to please the li-ons ___ this

day?

I need a

brand new ___ friend ___ who does-n't both-er me, ___

I need a brand new ___ friend ___ who does-n't trou-ble me. ___

I need some-one ___ who, who does-n't

need me. ___

I see the bath-room is clear, ___ I think that some-bod-y's near, ___ I'm sure that some-one is fol - low-ing me. _____ Oh, yeah. ___ Why did you throw the Jack - of - Hearts ___ a - way? ___

98

Why did you throw the Jack - of - Hearts a - way? — It was the
on - ly card — in the deck that I — had left to play. —

And I'll

say it a - gain, — I need a brand new friend,

And I'll brand new friend, — the end. —

The Changeling.

Words: Jim Morrison. Music: The Doors.

Bright Rock Beat

change - ling ___ see me change. ___

I'm the air you breathe, ___ food you eat, ___

(Orch.)

friends you greet ___ in the swarm-ing street.

See me

to 2nd Coda

change, ___ see me change. ___

103

104

You're Lost, Little Girl.

The Doors.

We Could Be So Good Together.

The Doors.
© Copyright 1968 Doors Music Co. Rondor Music (London) Ltd 10a Parsons Green, London SW6 for the UK and Eire.

With a beat
(tacet)

Gm

We could be so good to-geth - er,   Yeh, so   good to-geth - er,

E7

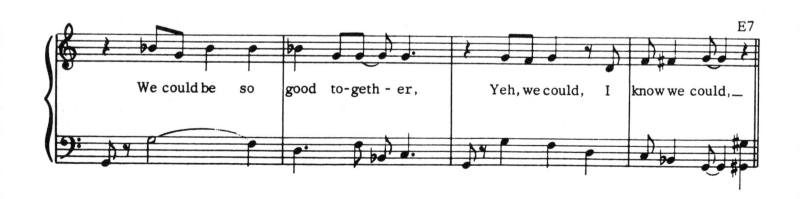

We could be so good to-geth - er,   Yeh, we could, I   know we could,__

good to-geth - er, Yeh, we could, know we could. __

We could be so good to-geth-er, Yeh, so good to-geth - er,

We could be so good to geth - er, Yeh, we could, know we could. __

Tell you lies, __ Tell you wick-ed lies, __

110

Strange Days.

The Doors.

down, _____ They're goin' to de-

stroy _____ our cas-

u - al joys, _____ We

shall go on play - ing or find _____

_____ a new town. _____

Strange

eyes fill strange rooms, ___

voic - es will sig - nal their ti - red

end, ___ The host

ess   is   grin - ning,   her

guests   sleep   from   sin - ning,

Hear   me   talk   of   sin   and   you

know   this is   it.

it.

Strange days have found us
And through their strange hours
We linger alone,
Bodies confused,

Memories misused,
As we run from the day
To a strange night of stone.

115

Love Me Two Times.

The Doors.

Love me two times, ba - by. Love me twice to-day;-

Love me two times, girl,

Love me one time,   Could not   speak;

Love me   one time,   Yeh,   my knee   got

weak.   Love me two times, girl,

Last   me   all   thru the   week;

People Are Strange.

The Doors.

No one re-mem-bers your name ___ when you're strange ___

when you're strange ___ when you're strange. ___

(to 3rd ending)

when you're down. ___

when you're strange. ___

The Crystal Ship.

The Doors.

1. bliss, an - oth-er kiss, (kiss,) an - oth - er kiss.
2. sane, we'll meet a - gain, (gain,) we'll meet — a -
3. why you'd rath-er cry, (cry) I'd rath - er fly.

2. The gain.
4. The

3. oh,

time; when we get back, ___ I'll ___ drop a line. ___

The Unknown Soldier.

The Doors.

125

(repeat and fade)

Ship of Fools.

Words: Jim Morrison. Music: The Doors.

Moonlight Drive.

The Doors.

moon - light drive ___

Let's swim ___ to the moon ___ uh huh Let's climb ___ thru the tide, ___

___ sur - ren-der to the wait - ing worlds ___ that

lap a - gainst our side ___ noth-in' left o - pen and no

time to de-cide ___ we've stepped in - to a riv - er on our

(repeat and fade)

L.A. Woman.

The Doors.

Bright beat

I see your hair is burn - ing__

hills are filled with

fi - re;__ If they

say I nev - er__ loved you__

you know they are a li - ar.__

lone, _____ so a - lone, _____ so a - lone, so a - lone. ___ Mo - tel mon-ey mur - der mad - ness let's change the mood from glad ___ to sad - ness.

142

Take It As It Comes.

The Doors.

Time to live, Time to lie,
Time to walk, Time to run,

Time to laugh, Time to die.
Time to aim your ar-rows at the Sun.

Chorus

Take it eas-y, ba-by, Take it as it comes.

Don't — move too fast If you want your love to last. You've been

mov - in' much too fast.

(Solo)

Go real slow, You'll like it more and more,

Take it as it comes. Spe-cial-ize in hav-in' fun._ (to Chorus)

Coda

mov-in' much too fast, Mov-in' much too fast,

Mov-in' much too fast._____

146

Wintertime Love.

The Doors.

Soul Kitchen.

The Doors.

Chorus

sleep all __ night in your soul kit-chen, __ warm my mind near your gentle stove. Turn me out and I'll wan - der, ba - by, stum-bling in the ne - on groves. Your fin-gers weave quick mi - na - rets, speak-ing in se - cret al - pha - bets. I light an -oth-er ci-ga - rette,

153

Roadhouse Blues.

Words: Jim Morrison. Music: The Doors.

155

roll ___ ba-by, roll; ___ let it

Repeat 3 times

Yeah, let it

roll, ___

all night long.

Ash-en la - dy,

Ash-en la - dy,

give up your vow!

Give

up your vow! ___

Save our cit-y,

Save our cit-y, right now!

When I woke up this morn-in' I got my-self a beer.

1.
When I

2.
The

fu-ture is un-cer-tain and the end is al - ways near.

Let it

B7 C7 C#7 D7 Eb7 E N.C. E E9

all night long.

Land Ho!

Words: Jim Morrison. Music: The Doors.

from liv - in' on the land.____
and old time lib - er - ty,____

Got to find my ship-mates____ and walk on for - eign sands."
Songs of love and songs of death, __ and songs to set men free.

C   A   D   C   A

G   1. F#m   Em

A7   2. F#m   Em

get my hands on a dol-lar bill,__ gon-na buy a bot-tle and
get my hands on a num-ber five,__ gon-na skin that lit-tle

1. drink my fill. If I
2. girl a-live._ If I get my hands on a

num-ber two come back home__ and mar-ry you,__

mar-ry you,_ mar-ry you._ All right!

Land _____ Ho!

Repeat and fade

161

End of the Night.

The Doors.

Cars Hiss By My Window.

Words: Jim Morrison. Music: The Doors.

I got this girl be-side____ me, but she's____

out of reach.____

Head-lights____ thru my win-dow____ shin-ing on ____ the wall____

Head-lights____ thru my win-dow____ climb-ing on ____ the wall,____

165

Can't hear my ba - by

tho' I call___ and call.___

Win - dow___ starts to trem - ble _____ with a son - ic boom.

Yes, The River Knows.

The Doors.

169

Please be - lieve me __ the riv - er told me __ ver - y soft - ly want you to hold me. __

go-ing but I need a lit-tle time, I

prom-ised I would drown my-self in mys-tic heat-ed wine.

D.S. al Fine

poco rall.

172

Touch Me.

The Doors.

Not To Touch The Earth.

The Doors.

House up-on the hill, Moon is ly-ing still, Sha-dows of the trees,

wit-ness-ing the wild breeze. Come on, Ba-by, run with me, Let's run

Drums

run with me, run with me,

run with me Let's run.

Voice

The

man-sion is warm at the top of the hill,__ Rich are the rooms and the com-forts there__

Red are the arms of lux - u - ri-ant chairs,__ And you don't know a thing till you get in-side__

Voice

Orchestra

Dead

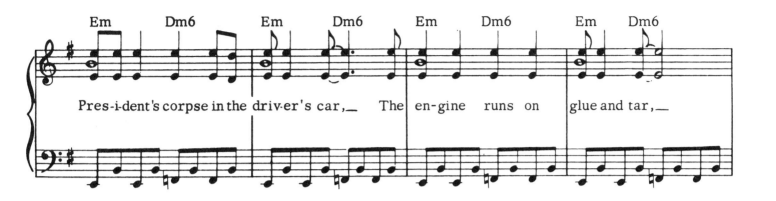

Pres-i-dent's corpse in the driv-er's car,_ The en-gine runs on glue and tar,_

Come on a-long, Not go-in' ver-y far, To the East_ to meet the Czar._

Run with me, Run with me,

Run with me. Let's run.

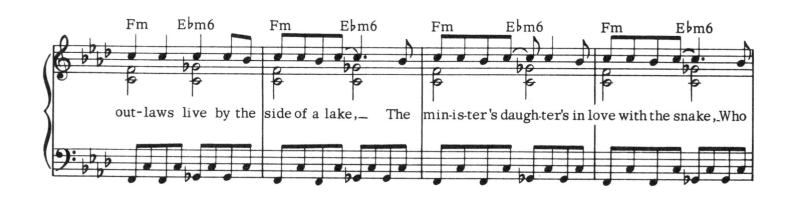

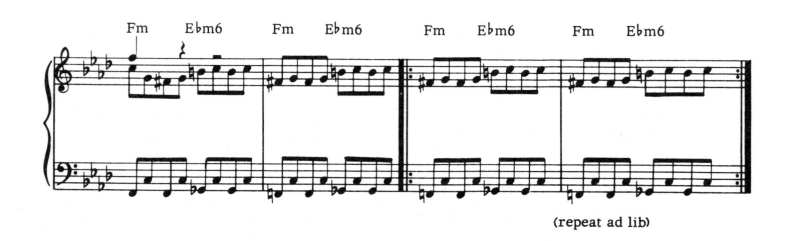

(repeat ad lib)

I Can't See Your Face In My Mind.

The Doors.

183

The W.A.S.P. (Texas Radio and the Big Beat).

Words: Jim Morrison. Music: The Doors.

Medium 4 beat

(spoken:) I want to tell you about Texas Radio and the big beat.

It comes out of the Virginia swamps, cool and slow, with a back beat,

narrow and hard to master.

some call it heavenly in its brilliance
others, mean and rueful of the Western dream
I love the friends I have gathered together on this thin raft
we have constructed pyramids in honor of our escaping.

This is the land where the
Pharaoh died.

(repeat ad lib)

The Negroes in the forest, brightly feathered, and they are saying:

"Forget the night!
live with us in forests of azure,
out here on the perimeter, there are no stars.

Out here we is stoned - immaculate."

(Sung:)
1. Lis-ten to this I'll tell you a-bout the heart-aches; I'll
2. Lis-ten to this I'll tell you a-bout Tex - as; I'll

tell you a-bout the heart-ache and the loss of God. ____ I'll
tell you a-bout Tex - as Ra - di - o. ____ I'll

Five To One

The Doors.

With a beat

188

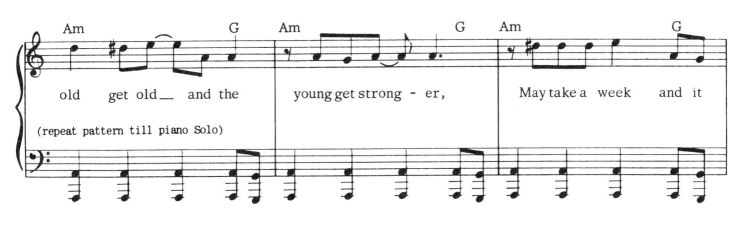

old get old___ and the | young get strong - er, | May take a week   and it

(repeat pattern till piano Solo)

may take long - er, | They got the guns but | we got the num-bers.

Gon-na win, yeh, we're | tak-in' o - ver, come on.

(Solo)

Your ball-room days are o - ver, ba - by,   Night is draw-ing near,

Sha-dows__ of the   eve - ning__   grow a - cross the year.__

191

Maggie M'Gill.

Words: Jim Morrison. Music: The Doors.

Slow 4

Voice

Miss Mag-gie M'- Gill __ she lived on a hill; __ Her dad-dy got drunk __ and left her no will, __ So she went down, __ Down to "Tan - gie Town." __ Peo-ple down there __ real-ly like to __ get it on. __

195

Summer's Almost Gone.

The Doors.

where will we be?

2.

Sum-mer's al-most gone, Sum-mer's al-most gone

We had some good times but they're gone.

The win-ter's com-ing on, sum-mer's al-most gone.

Queen Of The Highway.

Jim Morrison & Robbie Krieger.

3. American boy, American girl,
   Most beautiful people in the world!
   Son of a frontier Indian Swirl,
   Dancing thru the midnight whirl-pool
   Formless hope it can
   continue a little longer.

Unhappy Girl.

The Doors.

in a pris - on   of your   own de - vice. And you

can't be - lieve____   what it does to me____   to

see you   cry - in'.

- on   of your   own___ de - vice.

- on   of your   own ___ de - vice.

Easy Ride.

Jim Morrison.

The mask that you wore my fing-ers would ex-plore costume of con-trol ex-cite-ment soon un-folds_____ And I____ know it will be an Eas-y Ride,

yeah,   joy   fought

vague - ly   with   your   pride

with   your____   pride

(repeat and fade)

Blue Sunday.

Jim Morrison.

Now I have found my girl.___ My

girl a-waits for me in ten-der time.___

My girl is mine, She is the world, she is my

girl. My girl.___

My Wild Love.

Words: The Doors.
© Copyright 1968 Doors Music Co. Rondor Music (London) Ltd 10a Parsons Green, London SW6 for the UK and Eire.
All Rights Reserved. International Copyright Secured.

My wild love went riding,
She rode all the day;
She rode to the devil,
And asked him to pay.

The devil was wiser.
It's time to repent;
He asked her to give back,
The money he spent.

My wild love went riding,
She rode to sea;
She gathered together
Some shells for her hair.

She rode on to Christmas,
She rode to the farm;
She rode to Japan
And re-entered a town.

My wild love is crazy
She screams like a bird;
She moans like a cat
When she wants to be heard.

She rode and she rode on
She rode for a while,
Then stopped for an evening
And laid her head down.

By this time the weather
Had changed one degree,
She asked for the people
To let her go free.

My wild love went riding,
She rode for an hour;
She stopped and she rested,
And then she rode on.

When The Music's Over.

The Doors.

Rock 4

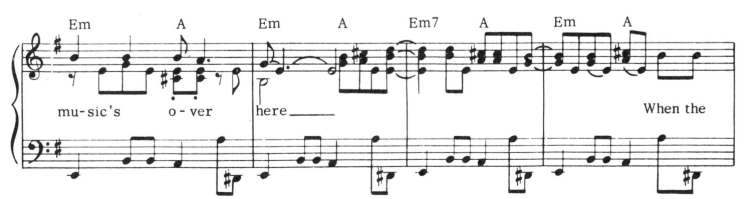

215

Be - fore I sink __ in-to the big sleep __

I want to hear __ I want to hear __

the scream of the but-ter-fly. __

Come back, ba - by, back in-to my arms.

(Chant - spoken over "Em - A9" chord patterns.)

We're getting tired of waiting around.
Waiting around
with our heads
to the ground.

I hear a very gentle sound.

What have they done to the earth?
What have they done to our fair sister?

Ravaged and plundered
and ripped her and bit her
Stuck her with knives
in the side of the dawn
and tied her with fences
and dragged her down.

I hear a very gentle sound.
With your ear down to the ground—

We want the world and we want it
Now!

Persian night!
See the light!
Save us!
Jesus!
Save us!

Love Her Madly.

Words: Robbie Krieger. Music: The Doors.

Bright Rock Beat

Don't you love her mad - ly? Don't you need her bad-ly?

Don't you love her ways? Tell me what you say?

(Repeat and fade)

Horse Latitudes.

Words: The Doors.

When the still sea conspires an armor
And her sullen and aborted
Currents breed tiny monsters,
True sailing is dead.

Awkward instant
And the first animal is jettisoned,
Legs furiously pumping
Their stiff green gallop,
And heads bob up
Poise
Delicate
Pause
Consent
In mute nostril agony
Carefully refined
And sealed over.

The Spy.

Jim Morrison.

Moderately Slow

Voice

I'm a spy___ in the house of love.___ I___ know the dream___ that you're__ dream - in' of;___ I___ know the word

that you long to hear. I know your

deep-est se-cret fear. I'm a spy,

I know ev-'ry-thing: Ev-'ry-thing you do;

Ev-'ry-where you go; I'm a spy,

Ev-'ry-one you know. I'm a spy,

I know your deep-est se-cret fear.

224

Alabama Song.

Music by Kurt Weill. Words by Bertolt Brecht.

229

Back Door Man.

Words & Music by Willie Dixon.

1. Oh yeah___ oh man,___
(Verse 2 see block lyric)

I'm a back door man___

I'm a back door man,

the men don't— know— what your lit-tle girls—— un-der-stand.—

And all your peo-ple, they're

try-ing to sleep,— I'm out to make her with my mid-night creep,—

yeah,— 'cause I'm a back door man.—

The men don't know,— what your lit - tle girls— un - der - stand..

Guitar solo

To Coda ⊕

Verse 2:
You men eat your dinner
Eat your pork and beans
I eat more chicken any man ever seen
Yeah yeah
I'm a back door man
The men don't know
But your little girls understand.

Well I'm a back door man
I'm a back door man
Oh, baby
I'm a back door man
The men don't know
But your little girls understand.

Crawling King Snake.

Words & Music by John Lee Hooker & Bernard Besman.

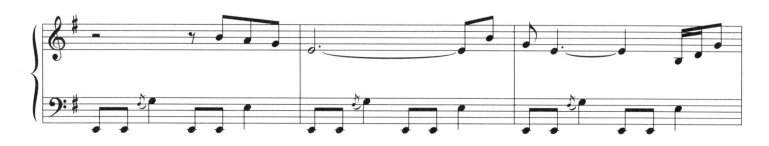

1. Well I'm the

D.%. al Coda

⊕ *Coda*

Verse 2:
Come a' crawling by my window grass is very high
Keep on crawling till the day I die
Crawling King Snake and a room of damned
You'd better give me what I want, gonna crawl no more.

Verse 3: Instrumental

Verse 4:
Come a' crawling baby, crawling round your door
See anything I want, I'm gonna crawl on your floor
Let's crawl in the room of damned
Come on give me what I want, ain't gonna crawl no more.

Verse 5:
Come on crawl, come on crawl
You don't have to get on your hands and knees baby
Crawl all over me
Just like the spider on the wall, we go crawl.

Verse 6:
Well I'm the Crawling King Snake in the room of damned
Call me the Crawling King Snake in the room of damned
You don't mess 'round with my mate
Gonna use her for myself.

Indian Summer.

Jim Morrison & Robbie Krieger.

I ____ love ____ you

best,   Bet - ter than____

all   the____

rest.

6/99(34404)